CHILDREN OF FOREIGN LANDS

By Elizabeth F. McCrady

Verses by Kate Cox Coddard

·NEW·YORK·
·THE·PLATT·&·MUNK·C^o^ INC·

OLGA, OF NORWAY

"Father, may I go fishing with you today?" asked Olga, a little girl who lives in Norway.

"Yes," said her father, "you may come along, but you must put on your warmest clothes."

In a few minutes Olga was ready. You could only see two blue eyes and a little nose, in a bundle of wool. I have never tried to fish in the winter time, have you? Let's see how Olga's father did it.

Olga and her father slipped their feet into the loops on their long, narrow skis. They carried long sticks, to help keep their balance. Then they went skimming over the top of the deep snow. Norway is a country so far north, that they have deep snow all winter. Olga learned to ski, almost as soon as she learned to walk.

Soon they came to a fjord. A fjord is a long, narrow in-
let from the sea. In summer, boats sail on the green water
of the fjords, between high mountains. There are many
beautiful fjords in Norway. They are deep and narrow.

There were ice boats and ice skaters on the fjord. Fish were swimming under the ice. How could they be caught? First, Olga's father chopped a round hole in the ice. Then he put beside the hole, a stick that could easily be bent. That was to be his fishpole. He tied his fishing line to that. There were many hooks on the line. Each hook was a bright color. Down into the water went the hooks without any bait.

"Now we shall wait for a bite," said Olga's father. "This tent I have put on the ice will keep the cold wind from us."

Suddenly her father said, "Look, Olga, the pole is wiggling up and down." Olga watched him pull the line up out of the water. On it there were many wiggly, waggly fish.

"One, two, three, four, five, six, seven, eight, nine, ten, eleven, twelve!" Olga counted. "I wish I could catch twelve fish at one time."

"You can," answered her father, "but first we must take

these fish off the hooks." Off came the slippery fish and zip, into a basket.

All afternoon Olga and her father took turns fishing, until they had all the fish they could carry. It was dark when they started home. The winter days in Norway are very short. "See the northern lights!" said her father.

Olga smiled and said, "I am glad I live way up north. I look for the northern lights every winter night. I pretend that the sky fairies, dance along those beautiful streaks of pink and yellow and white in the sky."

"To me," said her father, "they look like bright ribbons in the sky."

Northern lights are caused by electricity in the air. There are strange gases in the air near the north pole. When the electricity strikes these gases, it causes many beautiful colors to appear in the sky.

Olga and her father ate some of their fish for dinner. With it they ate such strange looking bread. It was large and round and quite flat. It is called fladbrod.

One day her mother said, "Spring is coming. The days

are getting longer. The snow has melted off the mountains.
To-morrow we will take the animals to the fresh, green
grass up there."

Olga was glad is was time to go to the dairy pasture, in

the mountains. All winter long she had played with the toys, her father had carved for her out of wood. Now she could be in the lovely green mountains and play on the moss, beside the sparkling streams.

Early the next morning, a long parade of farm animals started up the mountains. There were horses and cows, and calves and sheep and goats and pigs. In front of the parade the head milkmaid rode on a horse. She sat on a high saddle. She wore a white kerchief on her head.

Olga walked behind the animals, with her lunch on her back. With a heavy stick she kept them in line. Up, up, they went over the stony mountain roads. Finally they came to the saeter, the dairy farm in the mountains. How happy Olga was to see the saeter log cabin, with flowers growing on its grass roof. In the distance she could see snow-capped mountains.

All summer her work seemed like play to her. Every morning and evening, she helped milk the cows and goats. Then the milk was put in a small barrel, or churn. Olga turned the handle round and round and round, until it turned to butter.

Sometimes goat cheese was made in large, iron pots. When the water in the goat's milk had boiled away, the milk turned brown. Goat cheese looks like big pieces of brown soap. Milk was put away in wooden tubs, until it turned into cheese. There was white, yellow and pink cheese. Every one on the saeter, was kept busy from morning till night, storing food for the long winter.

Olga liked to help in the hay fields. She picked up the hay and put it on the wooden racks. There the sun and air dried it. Hay was sent down to the lowlands, on a heavy wire with pulleys.

In the evening Olga blew on her birch-bark horn. When the animals far away heard it, they came to her.

Some days in June were so long, there was no night at all. At midnight the sun shone brightly. At times children from another saeter came to see Olga. Olga played her musical horn and the children danced on the moss. They had many good times, picking wild flowers and berries.

There came a day when summer was over. Tubs filled with cheese and butter were packed on the horses. The parade started down to the red farm house, with its many little sheds in the lowlands. There the butter and cheese, would be stored in the wooden storehouse, or stabbur for the long cold winter. Olga said, "Farvel" (farewell) to the saeter she loved so dearly.

ELIZABETH F. McCRADY

OLGA OF NORWAY

Olga beams with happiness
When sliding on her skis.
She has learned to do it well
Just watch her bend her knees.

She tends sheep in the summer
Is outdoors all day long,
While working on the saeter
No wonder she is strong!

K.C.G.

CHING LING AND TING LING

Ching Ling is a little boy who lives in China. Ching Ling has a chubby little sister. Her name is Ting Ling.

Every day Ching tells Ting, about something he did in school that day. One day after school Ching cried, "Ting, look, look!" Ting ran to see what he had to show her. Ching unrolled a piece of paper. On it were two Chinese words. They did not look like our words. They looked like designs. "I learned to write these today," said Ching. "I made them with brush and ink."

"Oh, please show me how you made them," asked Ting.

Ching was happy to do that. He took from his silk purse a thick, flat stick of dried ink. It looked like licorice. He rubbed the dried ink in a few drops of water, on a flat stone. Then he painted this ✚ , like two sticks crossed.

"That means ten," said Ching. Then he painted this sign ✳ . "That means rice." Ching must learn thousands of such picture letters, because Chinese do not have ABC's as we have.

"I'll be glad when I am old enough to go to school," sighed Ting.

"Now, little sister," said Ching, "come with me. I am going to fly my new kite."

Soon Ting and Ching were walking up the hill with the kite. Ching's shaved head shone in the sunlight. His pigtail, or queue, bobbed up and down as he walked. Finally he said, "Now, watch my bird of happiness." The kite did look like a bird. It had green eyes, red wings and a striped purple and blue tail. "I call it my bird of happiness," said Ching, "because it sings when it flies through the air."

Ting's small, slanting eyes looked puzzled as she said, "I didn't know a kite could sing."

"This bird of happiness can," answered Ching. "Just listen when she is flying high." Ching unwound the kite string that was around a stick. Along came a rushing breeze. It lifted the bird of happiness. Together the

breeze and the bird went dancing, prancing in the sunlight.
"Listen, Ting," said Ching.

Ting cocked her head on one side and listened.   Then
she smiled and said, "I hear the bird." Sure enough a
lovely, soft whistling sound floated down from the sky.
"What makes the paper bird sing?" asked Ting.

"I fastened a reed onto the kite," explained Ching. "It is
a piece of coarse grass. When the wind blows on the reed,
it makes that lovely sound."

"The bird is dancing to the music," said Ting looking so
pleased.

Ching laughed. He looked up at his kite.   "Yes, it is
hopping around like a dancing bird."

Just then Ching and Ting saw something strange, walking up the hill. It looked like a big goldfish, but of course,
a goldfish can't walk up hills. It was a big, paper kite. Be-

hind it was a little boy. "Let's have a battle with our kites," said the little boy, whose name was Ho.

"Oh yes," agreed Ching, "let's try to cut each other's kite string in half."

"How can you do that?" asked Ting.

"Look here," said Ho. "I dyed the string black so that it can easily be seen, when the kite is flying. Then I glued powdered glass to it. That makes the string sharp enough

to cut another one." Ting still looked puzzled but she waited and watched.

Soon Ho had his bright goldfish swimming through the air. "I hear a tinkle, tinkle," said Ting. "What is it?"

"That is from the bells fastened on my kite," explained Ho.

Now Ho and Ching held tightly to their kite sticks. Each one wanted to win the battle. Each wanted to prove his skill.

Now the fish and bird were side by side. Ho tried to work his string over Ching's string. Ching tried to cross Ho's string with his own sharp one.

The bird flew up and down, back and forth. The goldfish darted forward and backward, now sideways, now up and down. The bells tinkled merrily. The whistle made

sweet sounds. Ting jumped up and down with excitement. Ching and Ho were breathless.

Suddenly the bird of happiness flew up, up in the air. It had been cut free. Ho's goldfish had won the game. Ching was sorry he had lost, but he was a good sport. He praised Ho for his skill.

Ting and Ching looked a little sad, as they watched that beautiful bird-kite fly away. The wind was carrying it over the hills. It seemed to get smaller and smaller. Now the bird of happiness was out of sight.

Then Ho, Ting and Ching started to walk slowly down the hill.

"I'll help you make a new kite," said Ho.

"That would be kind of you," said Ching. "I'll buy some rice paper, bamboo sticks, paste, and string tomorrow. See, I have saved some money." He reached in his pocket and

pulled out a string. On the string were four Chinese pieces
of money. They had square holes in the center. That is
why they could be carried on a string.

Ching and Ting were hungry when they ate their rice

dinner that night. The Chinese eat rice every day. Sometimes, when Chinese meet along the street, instead of saying, "How do you do?" they say, "Chihfahn," which means "Have you eaten rice?" Ching and Ting lifted their bowls of rice and meat to their lower lips. Then they pushed the food into their mouths with chopsticks. The Chinese use chopsticks, instead of forks and spoons.

After dinner it was story time. Their father read a story to them. He started from the back of the book. He read up and down on the page, instead of back and forth. That is the way the Chinese read.

Soon Ting's head nodded. Ching was sleepy, too. They had had a busy day. Off they went to bed. You would never guess of what their beds are made. They are made of bricks! In winter a fire is made under the brick beds to keep the sleepers warm. Now Ching Ling and Ting Ling have been tucked safely under soft covers. Let's say, "how foon." That means "good night" in Chinese.

ELIZABETH F. McCRADY

CHING LING AND TING LING

See the kite that Ching Ling holds,
I'd like to watch it fly
On its long and strong string,
Above his head so high.

See small Ting Ling's straight black hair,
It's plaited in a queue.
Her slanting eyes are twinkling,
She likes to fly kites too.

K.C.G.

WILHELMINA OF HOLLAND

Wilhelmina lives on a boat. The boat is in a canal in Holland. Holland is a low, flat country in Europe. It has many canals and ditches. Water from lakes and rivers and wet land runs into the ditches. That leaves the land between the ditches dry for gardens and houses.

Wilhelmina rides up and down the canal every day in the summer. In winter, when the boat is frozen in, she skates on the ice. Everyone in Holland skates on the canals. Children skate to school. Men skate to work. Women skate to the market.

In summer, Wilhelmina's father takes cheese from farms to the city in his boat. Sometimes he takes vegetables. Sometimes he takes blocks of black earth called peat. People in Holland burn peat instead of coal or wood. Sometimes he just takes passengers.

Wilhelmina has a friend named Katy. She lives in a red house beside the canal. She often rides to the city with Wilhelmina, but she has never lived on a boat.

Wilhelmina has never lived in a house on dry land. Her

home is pulled through the water by a horse with a large rope. Her brother Jan rides the horse along a path beside the canal. Her father sits in the front of the boat and steers it under bridges.

One day Katy stood at the door of the red house and called to Wilhelmina. "Mother would like to have you spend the night with me," she said. Wilhelmina's mother said she might go. So Jan stopped the horse and Wilhelmina stepped ashore. She climbed the steps to the top of the bank beside the canal. There Katy was waiting for her.

Then klomp, klomp, klomp, went the wooden shoes of the two little girls along the ground to the house. No wonder Dutch children call their shoes *klompen*. Outside the house they left their klompen as all Dutch people do. Wooden shoes make too much noise and dirt in the house. The Dutch scrub and scrub to keep their houses clean and bright. Wilhelmina and Katy walked in their stocking feet over the white sand on the floor.

"Mmmmmm, I smell something good," said Katy.

"So do I," said Wilhelmina. They were right. They found Katy's mother making cookies in the clean white kitchen.

"You may have these for a picnic," she said, "as soon as you have delivered the milk."

So Katy and Wilhelmina fastened a big dog named Hans to a bright, yellow cart. In the cart were brass cans full of fresh milk.

"Rattle, rattle, rattle" went the cart along the road.

"Klomp, klomp, klomp," went four little wooden shoes.

"Bow-wow-wow" barked Hans as he pulled the cart from house to house. When the cans were empty, Katy and Wilhelmina went home.

Katy's mother gave them cookies and cheese and milk for

a picnic. They took their lunch and their dolls and went into the fields. In Holland fields have ditches around them, instead of fences. Soon the black and white cows saw two little girls sitting beside a ditch splashing their bare feet in

the water. They were giving their dolls rides in their wooden shoes.

"Let's look for pictures in the water," said Wilhelmina. "Mother calls them reflections."

"I see two little girls with white caps on their heads," said Katy.

"I see a big bird flapping its wings," said Wilhelmina.

"Oh, it's a stork!" exclaimed Katy. "I hope it will fly to our house and build a nest in the wagon wheel Father put on the roof. That would bring us good luck."

After supper Katy's father told them stories about their country. He told how the North Sea used to spread over the land and drown whole cities full of people. He told how great walls, called dikes, were built to keep water from spreading over the land. He told about a street in Yaandam that had four hundred windmills on it. He told them Bible stories about the pictures on the tiles in the fireplace.

When it was bedtime he opened a sliding door in the wall. Behind it was a high bed that looked like a shelf.

Our two little blue-eyed Dutch girls slept there all night.

The next morning Katy's mother gave her some tarts. "Please take these to the house next door," she said. "They have a new baby there."

On the door knob of the house next door Katy and Wilhelmina saw a red ball.

"The new baby is a boy," said Katy. "If it were a girl the ball would be pink."

From there, Katy and Wilhelmina went to the tulip fields. The fields were as gay as a rainbow. There were red and white and purple and pink and yellow tulips. Holland is the tulip garden of the world. Katy and Wilhelmina helped the men cut the blossoms.

When Wilhelmina's house boat came, the tulips were loaded on it, to be taken to the market in the city. As they rode down the canal Katy and Wilhelmina saw many other

boats loaded with tulips. The next day was Tulip Sunday in Holland. Everyone would have tulips in the house.

In the market place Wilhelmina and Katy had such fun. They saw piles of cheese that looked like oranges. They watched the porters carry the cheese on trays into the Weigh House. There they were weighed on the scales. They watched the storks eat the fish left on the ground in the fish market. They threw bread to the ducks in the canal. They listened to the music of the bells in the Weigh House tower. Too soon it was time to leave.

That night Katy slept alone in her bed in the red house beside the canal. Wilhelmina slept in her bed in the house boat on the canal. She looked out of the window, with its white curtains and tulip box, and watched the lights in the houses. There seemed to be lights in the water, too. Wilhelmina went sound asleep with this picture of a fairyland in her mind.

ELIZABETH F. MCCRADY

WILHELMINA OF HOLLAND

Wilhelmina loves to skate,
All Holland children do.
She likes to watch the windmills
Against a sky of blue.

I'd like living on a boat
So small, and scrubbed, and neat,
But I'm afraid Dutch Klompen
Would hurt my little feet.

K.C.G.

KALA, A LITTLE HAWAIIAN BOY

Kala is a brown skinned boy who lives on the island of Oahu. Oahu is one of the Hawaiian Islands in the Pacific Ocean. Kala salutes the same red, white and blue flag that we salute, because the Hawaiian Islands belong to the United States.

Some of Kala's teachers are from the United States. Kala speaks English as well as we do. He also speaks the Hawaiian language. In the Hawaiian alphabet there are only twelve letters, a, e, h, i, k, l, m, n, o, p, u, w. How many letters are there in our alphabet?

One morning Kala's father said: "Kala, we need your help in the pineapple fields today. Come along with me."

Kala had sometimes helped to gather ripe pineapples,

but he had never helped to plant them. In the pineapple
fields he saw many long, wide strips of paper.

"How did you place the paper in such straight rows?"
asked Kala.

"We laid the paper on the ground yesterday with a machine," answered his father. "The edges of the paper are held down by loose earth. The paper will keep the weeds from growing up around the plants. It will also keep the roots damp and warm."

"But how can pineapples grow up through the paper?" asked Kala.

"That is going to be your job, Kala," said his father. "Here is a tool for you. If you make holes in the paper, I will put the plants through the holes into the ground."

"Oh, that would be fun" said Kala, his black eyes sparkling. So up and down the rows of heavy paper, Kala punched holes with the tool. His father went behind him and planted green pieces, that had been cut from ripe pineapple plants.

"In about twenty months," said Kala's father, "there will be hundreds of ripe pineapples here, one on each plant."

"That is a long time for the plant to grow," said Kala.

"The plant is low," replied his father, "but it grows slowly. The pineapple grows on top of a short, thick stem in a nest of stiff, sharp leaves. The best pineapples in the world are grown in the Hawaiian Islands. Most of them are canned before they are sent to other countries."

The sun was hot. Kala sang as he worked, for all Hawaiians like to sing. When he was thirsty he ran over to a palm tree to get a drink. Now, how could Kala get a drink from a tree? He ran up the trunk of the tree, holding on with his hands. Hawaiians can easily climb the trunks of the cocoanut trees because the trunks slope gradually. Kala came down with a brown cocoanut. He pulled off the husks and made two holes in the cocoanut shell. Then he held it up to his mouth. Down his hot throat

trickled the juice of the cocoanut. "Mmmmm," said Kala,
that tastes better than water."

After Kala and his father had worked a long time, Kala's
father said, "Let's have a swim in the ocean."

Kala's face beamed with smiles, for he would rather swim than do anything else. Children in Hawaii learn to swim when they are very young. Soon Kala and his father were splashing in the waves of the ocean. Each carried

with him a smooth board, called a surf-board. When Kala
got past the white splashing of the waves he stopped. He
waited for a big wave, then quickly threw himself full
length on the surf-board. The wave rolled nearer. Finally
it lifted Kala's surf-board on its crest. Then swiftly it carried the surf-board and its rider to shore.

"I wish I could stand on my surf-board," said Kala as he
watched his father ride his surf-board standing up.

"You can," his father answered, "if you try."

So the next time Kala tried to stand up on his swiftly
moving surf-board. He was almost straight up when he
lost his balance. He fell into the water and his surf-board
reached the shore without a rider.

"Oh, I can't learn to do that," said Kala.

"Yes, you can," said his father. "You must not give up
so easily. Try again."

So Kala tried again and again. Finally, he learned to stand on the board all the way to shore. That made him very happy and his father very proud.

When Kala got home he called to his little sister: "Liliha, Liliha, guess what I learned today. I learned to ride standing up on my surf-board, and I learned to plant pineapples. Now, close your eyes and hold out your hands and I'll give you a surprise."

Little Liliha held out her hands. Into them Kala dropped a lovely pink shell. When Liliha opened her eyes and saw the shell she gave a cry of delight.

"Now, Kala," she said, "I have a surprise for you. Close your eyes."

Kala closed his eyes. He felt a garland of flowers being put around his neck. When he opened his eyes he said, "Liliha, this is the prettiest lei I ever had."

Liliha looked pleased. "I gathered the brightest flowers I could find and made them into this lei for you," she said.

The two happy Hawaiian children went into their little house for dinner. They had fish, baked bananas and poi.

Poi is a pink porridge, made out of the roots of the taro plant.

After dinner father said, "How would you two children like to go to the largest island of the Hawaiian group to-morrow?"

"Oh," cried Liliha, "I have always wanted to go to the island of Hawaii."

"So have I," said Kala. "I have always wanted to see the mountain there, that pours out melted rock and steam."

"Very well," said their father, "I will take you. You will see the largest volcano in the world. It is like a huge bowl in the earth. The bottom of it is like a lake of fire."

Kala and Liliha were excited and happy. That night they said Aloha Oe, (farewell) to one pleasant day and looked forward to the dawn of the next.

ELIZABETH F. McCRADY

KALA OF HAWAII

Kala stands with outstretched arms
To take a surf boat ride,
Balancing most carefully
He sways from side to side.

Hawaiian boys are very strong
The highest trees they climb,
To bring down heavy cocoanuts
They have a happy time!

K.C.G.

MANUEL AND HIS FRIENDS
OF MEXICO

No, Manuel has not borrowed his father's hat. It is his very own. He does not think it a bit too large, for Manuel lives in Mexico, the land of big hats.

On the map, Mexico looks like a big cornucopia. If you should cut up our own United States into four parts, one of the parts would be as large as Mexico. There are only about seventeen million people in Mexico.

In Mexico you would find nearly everybody speaking the Spanish language. This is because long ago the Spaniards took the country away from the Indians they found there. For three hundred years they ruled over the country. Then Mexico decided to govern itself.

Some of the people of Mexico are pure Indians of the

same race the Spanish conquerors found there. Some are
the descendants of Spanish fathers and Indian mothers.
The rest are Spanish or people from other countries.

Even if Mexico is only a fourth as large as the United
States, there is too much of it to be seen in one trip. How

different the country will look to you as you go from one part to another.

Manuel lives up in the northern part, on a big plantation called a hacienda. It is owned by a very wealthy man who has hundreds of men working for him. Some of them raise grain and others care for sheep and cattle. Manuel helps tend the goats. He often rides about on a little donkey, called a burro, to keep them from straying away. When he grows bigger he will be a real cowboy.

Manuel's hat seems to be the biggest part of him. He calls it a sombrero. He is very proud of it. A Mexican thinks he must have a fine hat no matter how poor the rest of his clothes are. Often his hat costs from twenty-five to over a hundred dollars. Sombreros are made of felt or straw. The crown is high and peaked. The brim is sometimes as wide as your foot-ruler is long. It is often embroidered with gold and silver thread.

Next to his sombrero, Manuel thinks most of his serape.
The serape is a gaily striped blanket with a hole to let the
head through. In Mexico it takes the place of an over-
coat. Manuel wears clothes of coarse cotton under his
serape.

His mother's dress is of cotton, too, made with short
sleeves. She never wears a hat or shoes. Out of doors,
her head is covered with a brown shawl called a rebosa.
Sometimes her shawl is arranged so as to make a pouch
for Manuel's baby sister.

If Manuel's mother should invite you to dinner, do not
expect any bread and butter. You would have instead,
freshly baked tortillas or corn cakes. You would think
them rather tasteless, but Manuel's mother took a great
deal of trouble to make them. Kneeling on the floor she
ground the corn between two stones for many hours. Then
she patted the paste into cakes and baked them.

Let us say goodbye to Manuel and his mother and leave the dry plains with their prickly cactuses for another part of Mexico. Before we come to Mexico City, the capital of the country, there are miles and miles of great stiff plants growing far higher than your head. You may have seen a

single plant like these in the center of a wide lawn and
called it a century plant. Mexicans call it the maguey and
they think a great deal of it. No wonder, for the maguey
gives them all sorts of useful things, from a needle to a roof
for the house. In fact, the maguey is sometimes called the

thread and needle plant. If a little Mexican girl needs to mend her doll's dress she pushes one of the long thorns along the edges of the leaves of the maguey back into its sheath and then pulls it out. With it come tiny fibers. If she twists this thorn-needle just right, the fibers twine together to make a strong thread.

The Mexicans dry the leaves of the maguey to make roofs for their houses. They make ropes from the fibers of the leaves and braid them into mats for tables or chairs. They make a fire of the part of the plant which cannot be used for anything else and cook the roots over it, which they use for food.

But most of all, Mexicans grow the maguey plant for its juice. They call it "honey-water," and from it make a drink called pulque.

The people of Mexico take the juice from the plant in a very odd way. Just before the plant is ready to blossom,

they cut out the center of the stem. A hollow is left as big around as a washbowl. The sweet sap runs into this hollow. Two or three times a day little Alphonso comes with his father to get it. Alphonso's father puts one end of a long, thin gourd in the bowl of sap, then with his lips at the other end, he draws up the sap into the gourd. Then he pours the sap into a pigskin and hangs it over his shoulders, or carries it away in jars on a donkey's back.

As you leave the maguey plantation behind, you come into Mexico City. This beautiful city, like every other Mexican town, has a park called a plaza in its center. There is a bandstand where the people come evenings and Sunday mornings to listen to the music they love. A very large and beautiful cathedral faces the plaza. There are many fine churches in Mexico.

The houses with their high stone walls and heavy iron bars look very gloomy. Once there were many robbers in

Mexico, so the houses had to be barred. Inside the huge
door how different everything looks! The house is built
around a courtyard called a patio. There are trees, flow-
ering vines, a fountain and birds singing in cages. Carmen
and Miguel, the children of the family, play in the gar-

den. The grown-ups watch the fun from the porch around the patio.

Of course many Mexican children do not have such fine homes as Carmen and Miguel. The poorer people live in square, windowless huts of adobe or sun-dried brick. These huts are not very pretty but they are cooler in summer and warmer in winter than wooden houses.

Carmen and Miguel ask you to stay and share in their Christmas celebration. At Christmas time they march through the patio carrying lighted candles and singing. The best fun is the breaking of the pinate. The pinate is a great jar filled with candies, nuts and toys. The jar is covered with bright paper to make it look like a big doll or a bird. The children are blindfolded and take their turn at hitting at the jar. When at last it breaks, what a scrambling there is for the toys!

You would enjoy this frolic, but I am sure you would not exchange your own Christmas tree for a pinate.

MANUEL OF MEXICO

Manuel has a hat,
It is as big as he,
When he puts it on sometimes,
He can scarcely see.

Little boys of Mexico
Ride on burros too,
Their serape is a blanket
Which would cover most of you.

CHULA OF SIAM

Chula is a little boy who lives in Siam. Siam is a country in Asia. Sometimes it is called the Land of the White Elephant. Chula likes his country's flag better than any other flag in the whole world. It has single stripes of red, white and blue with a white elephant in a red circle in the center.

There are many elephants in Siam. There are dark gray ones and light gray ones. The dark gray elephants work in the forests. The light gray ones are called sacred white elephants. They are given to the king and are royally treated in a palace of their own.

There are also many little boys in Siam. Some of them drive big water buffalo when the rice fields are plowed. Then they wade in water, as they put the rice plants into the muddy ground. When the rice is ripe they take it to the city in boats. Rice is the most important crop grown in Siam.

Other boys and girls live in houseboats on the river.
When they want to buy something, they go in their teakwood canoes to a store floating on water. As they go up and
down the river they pass many beautiful temples. If a

canoe tips over they don't mind. They learn to swim as soon as they learn to walk.

Some boys live near great forests of teak trees. That is where Chula lives. Every year there are heavy rains and floods. Chula's house is on stilts made of teakwood. Teakwood has so much oil in it, that it does not rot in water. The stilts keep the house high and dry. The roof is made of palm leaves. In dry weather Chula's father keeps his animals under the house.

"Wake up," said Chula's father one bright morning. "We are going into the forest to cut timber."

Chula got up from his mat on the floor. The air was very hot. All he put on was his panung. A panung is a strip of colored cloth. Siamese boys and men tie panungs around their waists, instead of wearing trousers.

In a few minutes Chula and his father and two other men were on their way to the forest. When they came to a tall,

straight tree on a low hill, Chula's father stopped to look at it. Its leaves were dead.

"What is that ring around the trunk of the tree?" asked Chula.

"That is the girdle," said his father. "I cut the bark to make the tree die slowly. After it is dead it is light enough to float on water."

One man started to chop on one side of the tree, the other man chopped on the other side. The notches they made got bigger and bigger. At length the top of the tree moved a little. The men ran quickly. Then "crash" the big tree fell on the soft ground.

"Now, Chula," said his father, "help us chop the tree into logs."

The sun was very hot. As Chula chopped and chopped
he got so hot, that water dripped from his straight black
hair. It ran down his brown face and neck, to his brown
chest and back. All day he helped to make logs.

The next morning Chula was glad when his father said,
"Today we will take the elephants with us to the forest."
In a few minutes Chula sat on the back of his favorite ele-
phant. Chula had named his elephant Bumpo, because he

bumped logs into place with his ivory tusks and sometimes even with his head.

"I like you better than any other elephant in the whole world," whispered Chula, as Bumpo's big feet went crashing, crashing over the underbrush of the forest.

"Siam has more teak forests than any other country in the world," said Chula's father as he rode on his elephant. Chula said nothing. He was thinking how lucky he was to live near a teak forest in Siam.

"You start on the logs at that end," said Chula's father, when they came to the freshly cut logs on the ground. "And if Bumpo does not work, prod him with your stick."

But Bumpo knew what to do. He had been working in the teak forest for many years. With a chain Chula fastened a log to Bumpo's harness. The elephant dragged the log slowly for three miles, to the river bank. Then back

he went for another log. He used his trunk and his tusks to put the logs in a neat pile.

Back and forth, back and forth went the elephants, dragging logs to the banks of the river. Soon the logs would be floated down the river to the sawmill.

"I like to do this," said Chula to his father.

"Yes," said his father, "today the elephants are doing the hard work. But you must learn to like hard work too."

Finally Chula's father said: "Elephants are not as strong as they look. They should not work more than four hours a day." So Chula and Bumpo stopped working. Bumpo ate banana leaves and bamboo sprouts. Chula ate mangosteens, a fruit which grows in Siam.

Chula said: "Bumpo you are hot and tired. How would you like to have a bath in the river."

Bumpo nodded his head and looked pleased. He went

splashing into the water. First his feet were wet; then his
ankles; then his knees. He filled his trunk with water and
squirted it all over Chula. Chula liked the nice, cool
shower. Then Bumpo lay down in the river. Chula started

to scrub him with a brush of twigs. He scrubbed and scrubbed, until he had one side of Bumpo all clean, except his great big ear.

Just as he was trying to get to the ear Bumpo sneezed, "Kerchoo!" He sneezed so hard that he shook all over, and Chula slipped off his side "ker-splash" right into the water. As fast as he could, Bumpo stood up in the water and held out his trunk toward Chula. Then he lifted Chula out of the water and put him on his back. He walked slowly out of the river," "splash, splash, splash, splash."

On the way home Chula said, "Bumpo, you are a kind friend. I would rather have you, than the finest white elephant of the king's herd. You deserve a palace and robes of silk and jewels on your back."

Bumpo shook his head. He was thinking that he would rather work in the forest with Chula, than live in the finest palace in Siam.

Elizabeth F. McCrady

CHULA OF SIAM

Chula rides upon the trunk
Of this big elephant.
If we could only do it
We'd think it quite a stunt.

Little boys of far Siam
Wear bright striped panungs gay,
They don't have our many clothes
To put on every day.

K.C.G.

MARIA AND CARLOS OF SPAIN

"Maria, Maria," cried Carlos, a boy who lives in Spain.
"Come quickly, I have a surprise for you." Carlos was
walking through the iron gates, which led from the street
to the courtyard of his home. He looked up at the balcony
around the courtyard. From one of the rooms up there, his
little sister came running.

She soon stood beside her big brother, by the fountain in
the courtyard. The courtyard, in Spain is called the patio.
Around it the Spanish house is built. The patio is like a
garden. There are orange and lemon trees. There are
baskets of flowers hanging from the balconies around it.
There are cages filled with singing birds.

"Can you guess what I have for you?" asked Carlos.

"A red rose for my hair," Maria guessed, her black eyes flashing.

"No," answered Carlos.

"Perhaps you met a bacquillero on the street and paid

him to turn his wheel. When his wheel stopped, the hand
pointed to the number two, so he gave you two little cakes,
one for you and one for me. Am I right, Carlos?" asked
Maria.

"Wrong again," said Carlos. "Here it is." He took his
hands from behind his back. In them he held a box. It was
dripping wet. No wonder!

When Maria opened the box she cried, "Oh, goldfish!
Two beautiful goldfish for our fountain!"

"Let's put them into the fountain," Carlos said. So
he held the box upside down, over the little pool in the
patio. Splash, splash, went the two little goldfish into their
new home.

"Soon you will have a roof of blue sky," said Maria to
her new pets. "The awning over our patio will be taken
away, when the days grow cooler."

Spain is a country in Southern Europe and it gets very hot there. The hot part of the day is called "hours of fire." Then the children do not play in the streets but stay in the shade of the patio.

While Maria and Carlos were watching the goldfish, their father came to them. "I must drive to the vineyards today," he said. "Who would like to go with me?"

"I would," cried Maria, for she had never been to the vineyards.

"I would, too," said Carlos, "but I promised to be in a bull fight this afternoon." (He meant a pretend bull fight, of course.)

Soon Maria and her father were driving to the country. Maria's sharp eyes saw everything. Suddenly she said, "I see a walking straw stack."

"A walking straw stack?" said her father. "Who ever

heard of a walking straw stack?" He looked ahead and
there he saw a little mule so covered with straw, that it
did look like a straw stack. In Spain the mules carry all
sorts of things. They even carry children to school.

As they drove along, Maria and her father munched on ripe olives. Like all Spaniards, they like to eat olives wherever they go. There are so many olive orchards in Spain, that their olives are sent all over the world.

When they came to the vineyards Maria saw men, women, and children at work. They were picking bunches of pink and purple grapes from the vines and filling large baskets.

"Where are they going?" asked Maria, looking at the women carrying tall baskets on their heads.

"They are going to the sorting shed, to sort the grapes," answered her father. They will put the good ones into one wagon and the bad ones into another."

"There are some wagons filled with grapes," said Maria.

"Yes," answered her father. "Those are going to the wine-press. There the grapes are crushed to make wine."

Maria watched, while her father talked business with a man there. When they started home, her father gave her a large bunch of raisins. "You may eat these on your way home," he said. "They are grapes which have been dried."

"I'll save them for Carlos," said Maria. "He brought me a present this morning. I'll give him a present tonight."

Suddenly her face looked as bright as the sun and she cried, "Oh, I hear the piper, I hear the piper with his pigs. What a queer tune he is playing on his pipe!"

Down the road came a man, with many pigs trotting behind him. There were little ones and big ones, fat one and thin ones. There were many pink noses and curly tails.

"They have been looking for acorns, under the cork oaks in the mountain all day," said Maria's father. "Acorns make thin pigs fat and fat pigs fatter. The cork oak is a very useful tree."

"Why is it so useful?" asked Maria.

"Men cut the bark off the cork oaks every ten years," ex-

plained her father. "They soak it in water, then clean it and scrape it and heat it and press it out in flat sheets. After that the cork is made into stoppers, for bottles and many other things."

"Some of the pigs leave the others and run down different lanes," said Maria.

"Yes," answered her father, "each pig seems to know when he comes to his own home. He runs to it without being driven."

"There are the gypsies in their queen homes," said Maria pointing to caves, which the gypsies had made in the side of a rocky hill.

"Yes," her father replied, "and soon we shall be in our home. Each one thinks his home is best, doesn't he?"

That night after their dinner of tortillas, fruit and hot chocolate, Maria's father played his guitar while Maria danced in the patio. Carlos munched on the raisins Maria had given him, as he watched her. In her long velvet dress and lace mantilla, she looked like a little gypsy.

ELIZABETH F. McCRADY

MARIA AND CARLOS OF SPAIN

This dainty Spanish maiden
Is listening to a song,
For I am sure the yellow bird
Is singing all day long.

He warbles he likes sunshine
Spain's flowers and skies of blue,
Maria looks delighted
I'm sure that I would too.

K.C.G.

ABDUL, THE ARABIAN BOY

Abdul is a little boy who lives in Arabia. Arabia is a country in far away Asia. If we went to Arabia we would not see snow. We would not see tall buildings. We would not see green fields. We would not see many rivers. In Arabia we would see only sand and rocky hills.

Abdul lives on the sands of Arabia. One day he wakened very early. It was the day for his first trip to the village alone. He was so excited!

Soon he was on his way. He held a rope which was around a camel's neck. The camel walked lazily along the sand, loppity, loppity, lop. His funny head at the end of his long, shaggy neck jerked back and forth. Abdul's bare feet pattered softly over the sand. He wore a loose robe of wool, called an aba.

As the sun climbed higher, Abdul got hotter. He pulled the hood of his robe over his head, to keep the sun away. Soon he got thirsty and tired so he sat down for a rest. He took a drink of water from his goat-skin bag.

The camel looked down at Abdul out of the corners of his large, droopy eyes. His big, lower lip seemed to smile. He was hot, too, but he did not need water. He carries enough water to last for six days. He carries it in many little sacks inside his body. When he is thirsty the little sacks empty water into his stomach. That is why camels are used on the desert. Have you ever seen the hump on a camel's back? Under that hump he carries enough food, to last for many, many days.

As Abdul sat on the sand, along came a boy and a donkey. When the boy saw Abdul he said, "May Allah protect you."

Abdul replied, "May Allah grant you health." That is the way Arabs start to talk to each other. Then he said, "You look hot and thirsty. Would you like a drink of water?"

The boy, whose name was Hammed, said he would be glad to have one. "Are you going to the village?" asked Abdul.

"Yes," answered Hammed. So Hammed and his donkey, Abdul and his camel started for the village. "I live in a little

square, white house in the village," said Hammed. "Where do you live?"

"I live in a tent on the desert," answered Abdul. "Our tent is made of goat's-hair cloth. We do not live in the same place all year. My father has sheep and goats. We travel from one oasis in the desert to another. There we find grass and water for the animals."

"Is that a load of fire-wood on your camel?" asked Hammed.

"Yes," said Abdul, "my father told me that if I gathered fire-wood, he would let me sell it in the market all by my-self."

"How do you get fire-wood on the sandy desert" asked Hammed, for he knew that there were no trees on the desert.

"There is a tiny bush on the desert called sage brush," an-swered Abdul. "You cannot see much of it above the

ground. Below the ground it has very long roots. They grow way down looking for water. Yesterday I dug up the roots of many sage brush. Now you see them loaded on my camel. But you, too, have a heavy load."

"The baskets which my donkey is carrying are filled with olives. I have been in the olive orchard for three days and nights," said Hammed.

"You stayed there all night?" asked Abdul in surprise.

"Yes," answered Hammed, "we slept in a hut made of stone and mud. Each day the village women climbed ladders, to reach the olives on the trees. I climbed the trees. Sometimes I shook the branches. Then the big, black olives fell to the ground."

"Surely you don't eat all of these olives?" asked Abdul.

"No," laughed Hammed, "I am taking these to the mill. There they are crushed to make olive oil."

When the boys parted in the village, they said they hoped they would meet again.

Down through the narrow streets, Abdul walked with his camel. He was all tingly inside. This was an adventure for him. When he got to the market place, he sat down beside his camel and waited for someone to buy his firewood. He watched the donkeys and cows and sheep and camels and people crowded on the same street.

Suddenly Abdul heard a voice. He looked up. There stood an Arabian woman dressed in a brown robe. Abdul stood up. He could see the dark eyes, looking through the peep-hole, in the robe over her head. She bought some fire-wood from Abdul. Then he ate some dates for his lunch. Dates grow on palm trees in the desert.

Abdul sat in the market place, until he had sold all of his fire-wood. Then he wanted to buy a present for his mother, with the money he had earned. He tied the camel's front leg, so it would not wander away. Then he found a silver-smith's shop. There he bought a shiny, silver anklet for his mother. There were so many shops to see! He did not want to leave. He wandered slowly up and down the streets for a long time.

Then he climbed on his camel's back and started home. Out on the desert Abdul looked at the sky. It had turned to

a strange, yellow color. The wind began to blow. Closer and closer it came with a queer, whistling sound. In a few minutes it was beating into Abdul's face. He could not see a thing. His eyes and mouth were full of sand. The camel lay down and closed his nose and eyes. Abdul pulled his robe around him and hid behind the camel, until the wind stopped blowing. Then, again, they started for home. The sun had gone down. The air was cold. Abdul's wool robe kept him warm.

His mother and father were glad to see him. They were afraid he had lost his way. His mother was proud of the new silver anklet, which she put around her bare ankle.

Abdul's dinner was cooking in the fire-pot, in front of the tent. He ate lamb and drank goat's milk. He ate with his fingers as all Arabs do.

Abdul was tired when he lay down, on his bed of sheep skins that night. He fell asleep right away and dreamed that he was in the narrow streets of the village again.

ELIZABETH F. McCRADY

ABDUL OF ARABIA

Abdul dresses in a robe
His face is very tanned,
A camel lies beside him
Upon the sun-baked sand.

His tent, made of goats hair cloth,
Is large and deep and wide,
I would like to visit him
So I could peek inside.

K.C.G.